NIGHT LIFE

NIGHT LIFE

MALCOLM PENNY

Photographs from the Bruce Coleman
Wildlife & Travel Photo Collection

BOXTREE

First published 1993 by
Boxtree Limited
Broadwall House
21 Broadwall
London SW1 9PL

10 8 6 4 2 1 3 5 7 9

Designed by Sarah Hall

Colour reproduction by Dot Gradations, Chelmsford, Essex
Typeset by SX Composing Ltd, Rayleigh, Essex
Printed and bound by Bath Press Colourbooks, Glasgow

A CIP catalogue record for this book is available from the British Library

ISBN 1-85283-169-3

ACKNOWLEDGEMENTS

The photograph which appears on page 76 is reproduced courtesy of the
Natural History Photographic Agency © Ivan Polunin; illustration on page
120 by Heather Quinn. With these exceptions, all pictures courtesy of Bruce
Coleman Wildlife & Travel Photo Collection: Jen & Des Bartlett 40; Erwin
& Peggy Bauer 53, 66, 121; George Bingham 83; Mark N. Boulton 34, 50;
Jane Burton ii, 14, 32, 41, 46, 55, 58, 72, 78, 81, 87, 88, 90, 91, 96, 100,
107, 112, 117, 122; John Cancalosi 56, 98, 101b; Waina Cheng 37; Patrick
Clement 26, 54; Bruce Coleman 85; Alain Compost iii, 51, 92, 93, 106;
Gerald Cubitt 11, 47, 95; Mik Dakin 30; Adrian Davies 44; Jack Dermid 65,
74; Stephen J. Doyle 109; Ernest Duscher 67; M. P. L. Fogden 45, 75, 114;
Jeff Foott Productions 24, 38b, 52; C. B. & D. W. Frith 64; Frances Furlong
62, 104a; Frank Greenaway 60, 61; Udo Hirsch 71; Carol Hughes 59;
Stephen Krasemann 17; Felix Labhardt 68b; Gordon Langsbury 39; M. R.
Phicton 99, 103; Andrew J. Purcell 110; Hans Reinhard 73, 116, 119; Gary
Retherford 115; Alan Root 35; Frieder Sauer front jacket, 42, 77, 80, 105,
118; John Shaw 57, 68a, 69; James Steven 38a; A. J. Stevens 101a; D. & R.
Sullivan 70; Kim Taylor 6, 29, 36, 86, 108, 111, 120; Rod Williams 82, 102,
104b; Konrad Wothe 89, 94; Gunter Ziesler 22, 48, 84.

CONTENTS

INTRODUCTION

I am as uneasy in the dark as any other sighted human. This normal condition was aggravated when I was a student: I was beaten up one night in what, until then, I had thought of as a friendly city. For years afterwards I avoided the mediaeval alleys of the old town after dark, and stuck to the broad lamplit streets.

Then I went to work in the Seychelles, on the tiny island of Cousin. There, the darkness held no threats: there are no large predators, no venomous snakes – even the mosquitoes are free from disease. I came to love scrambling through the woods and up the little hill in the dark, recording the songs of brush warblers before dawn.

One early morning, before it was light, a sudden unearthly wailing gurgle descended on me from the dark sky. As it grew louder, my imagination went into a flat spin. My hair stood on end – it really does, you know, when we are frightened enough, thanks to our mammalian ancestors – and my heart raced. To this day, I don't know what I thought it was, falling on me from the tropical night. I think I screamed as a heavy object crashed into the bracken by my side. It was the season's first Audubon's Shearwater, returning to the island to breed after a year at sea. Later that week, hundreds more appeared.

Ornithologically, this was a fascinating discovery: but it was also the start of a train of thought which I am still riding to this day. In most parts of the modern world, the night holds no real dangers; but there is still a race memory, bred into us, which gives rise to irrational fears when things 'go bump in the night'. This is why I find nocturnal animals such an absorbing study.

MALCOLM PENNY

THE ARMIES OF THE NIGHT

Human beings live in the light. Our dominant sense organs are our eyes and we might accurately be called 'visual animals'. Small wonder, then, that as a species we are afraid of the dark. Yet, in the depths of a forest at night, or among the half-seen shapes of hedgerow or hillside, there exists an army of creatures to which the darkness is not alien.

Today, the building of cities and the cultivation of the land have tamed the wilderness; many would say they have destroyed large parts of it. But there are still areas of the world where darkness cloaks danger. In the forests of India, where tigers stalk their prey, in the African bush, where leopards hunt at night, even in the North American deserts, home of the pit vipers, or in the Alaskan wilderness, the range of the grizzly bear, there are creatures capable of harming humans. Where we are blind, they can see. Our senses of hearing and smell have been dulled by our dependence on vision: theirs are sharp, honed in the absence of light. A rattlesnake can locate its prey in total darkness, guided only by the ability to sense the warmth of its blood. The awe in which we hold animals like these – because they possess senses which we have all but lost, or have never had – is the key to our fascination with the life of the night.

Most habitats are exploited by more than one group of animals. After sunset, the diurnal population is replaced by the night shift. Between them, in the half-light, crepuscular animals flit and scuttle in the dusk and the dawn. It is the nocturnal element of this box and cox arrangement that concerns us here.

A CLOAK OF DARKNESS

Many animals have no choice but to live in the dark; some of them, such as shrews and mice, are vulnerable to predation by day. The world is full of diurnal predators, such as birds of prey and small cats, and darkness offers safety. Some animals are too conspicuous and immobile to function in the light. An orb-web spider building her web in an open place would be a natural target for birds; so most weave by night, leaving a trap which can still catch flying insects through the day. The spider hides close to the edge of the web, springing from cover only to remove her victims and whisk them, bound with silk, back into hiding to eat.

Moths fly by night for their own evolutionary reasons, having diversified to such an extent that they can exploit tiny niches characterized by very small differences in humidity or exposure. It may be significant that they alone among insects have evolved a specific defence against being caught at night in spiders' webs. The loose scales on their wings often enable them to fall free from a sticky web, leaving the scales stuck to the strands. The intensity of the evolutionary battle for supremacy is reflected in the small group of spiders which specializes in catching moths at night: they have evolved a web with a long sticky 'ladder' below the main disc, designed to make the fall so long that before a moth reaches the bottom it has no scales left to protect it. Other spiders produce fluffy silk which is not sticky at all, but entangles any insects, including moths, which come into contact with it.

Many animals seeking safety in the dark attract predators adapted to hunting them. The tiny rustles of shrews in the leaf-litter are detected by owls whose ears are positioned to improve the accuracy of their direction-finding. The warmth of a prairie dog's body enables a rattlesnake to find it in darkness, using sense organs evolved for the purpose. The agile flight of moths was the evolutionary inspiration for the even greater agility of bats, with their amazingly precise echo-location. Some predators can hear the slightest movement, and smell the subtlest scent, as they hunt for creatures that would hide from them in the night.

A HAVEN FROM THE HEAT

After the practicalities of hiding and hunting, the third reason for a nocturnal existence is physiological. 'Poikilothermic' animals, which cannot control their own body temperature by internal means, are liable to suffer during the day from over-heating. This threat is removed in the cool of the night. Many desert animals, especially reptiles and insects, but even including some mammals, which are 'homoiothermic' and theoretically in charge of their own internal temperatures, are nocturnal, also to avoid over-heating. Amphibians and molluscs, and those reptiles that lack an impermeable skin, avoid the daytime to conserve water. Even the floor of the desert may be humid enough for them at night, though in the heat of the day they would be dehydrated in minutes.

The kangaroo rats of the Californian deserts have evolved an ingenious way of retaining moisture during the day. They retreat into their burrows, taking with them a supply of the dry grass seeds which are their main food. The grass seeds are not to be eaten immediately: instead, they are stacked near the entrance to the burrow, where they absorb moisture from the kangaroo rat's breath as it dozes until dusk. When night comes, the rat eats the seeds before it again ventures out to look for food, thus recycling the moisture which would otherwise have been lost to the thirsty desert air.

Animals which are forced into a nocturnal existence by the demands of their physiology must evolve at least some of the sensory adaptations needed by all nocturnal animals if they are to find food and escape predators. Thus skinks and geckos, whose families are principally diurnal, exhibit the large eyes and sensitive hearing found in nocturnal animals.

SHARING THE NIGHT

A fourth reason for taking up a nocturnal life is less obvious than the others: it is to share a food supply. Nectar-feeding moths share the daytime food supply of butterflies, for example, and hippos graze at night on turf which during the day might be occupied by antelope and zebra. There are other reasons for being nocturnal: the animals are safer from attack by lions at night, and free from the danger of over-heating, which is a constant problem.

Among the fruit-eating monkeys of South and Central America, smaller species are at a disadvantage when groups converge on a tree in which the fruits are ripe. Because this is a seasonal as well as a localized food supply, there is considerable competition for it, and the larger and more aggressive species are likely to take the lion's share. The smaller species steal a march on them by eating the fruit before it is ripe, or by hanging around under trees, waiting for fruits dropped by the larger species. It is surprising that only one species of monkey, the Douroucouli or night monkey, has evolved to eat the fruits at night, while the others are asleep.

Ruminants, such as antelope and buffalo, gather food mainly during the day, but may be said to eat it at night, when it is processed in their complex four-chambered stomachs. Food which they gather during the day is hardly masticated at all, but transferred to the rumen, or first stomach, for storage. When it has been softened by bacteria, it is returned to the mouth, often at night, to be chewed more thoroughly. The second time it is swallowed, it goes to the second stomach, the reticulum, and from there to the third and fourth chambers, the manyplies and obamasum, where it is finally digested.

Thus ruminants are nocturnal feeders, even though they seldom gather vegetation in the dark.

Many nocturnal animals are selective in their periods of activity. Those that depend more on vision than on other senses are usually crepuscular, or at least active only during the earlier part of the night, not in the darkest hours before dawn. It follows that when they retire, they leave a vacant niche for other animals which can function in deeper darkness. Moth collectors who use lights to attract their specimens have long been aware that certain species appear at set times: the Small Tiger moth comes to light only at dusk and dawn, for example, while the Garden tiger never appears before midnight. This may be something to do with the latter's large size and bright colours in flight, and therefore the need to avoid crepuscular predators; but the effect is to subdivide the night into several feeding niches, not only spatially, in terms of food sources, but temporally as well. This also explains why there are so many species of moths that are only subtly different from one another; their world is divided not only into many distinct niches, but into several separate watches of the night.

SAFETY IN THE DARK

HIDING BY DAY

The first prerequisite for animals that seek safety under cover of darkness is, apparently paradoxically, the ability to remain hidden during the day. Once the sun comes up, the fact of having survived through the night would be rendered worthless if the survivor were to be immediately pounced upon and eaten by some diurnal predator. Thus the study of nocturnal animals must include some attention to the ways in which they survive in daylight.

Some simply hide. In burrows, under the bark of trees, under stones or fallen logs, under the leaf litter of the forest floor, or among the dense grass of meadowland, huge numbers of creatures lie motionless during the day, waiting for the return of darkness before they emerge once more to look for food or a mate. Some of these hiding-places are more secure than others. In the natural way of things, predatory species have evolved whose main source of food is seeking out just these hidden animals, often dormant and defenceless during the day. Blackbirds toss aside dead leaves in search of unsuspecting spiders and beetles; centipedes hunt through the grass stems for smaller invertebrates; woodpeckers drill for fully-grown insects as well as larvae under the loose bark of dead trees.

There are some real specialists in the search for nocturnal animals in their daytime retreats. Earwigs, and some predatory beetles, find food by a minute inspection of leaves and grass stems; and a small snake in Patagonia, the Fer-de-lance, has developed the art of moving not in the normal snake-like curves of its kind but in a straight line, the better to invade the narrow burrows of small rodents, sheltering during the day.

SURVIVING BY DECEIT

This steady pressure from predation has been the main factor in developing the other means by which nocturnal animals survive in daylight: camouflage. Individuals whose camouflage is not effective enough are less likely to survive to produce offspring than those whose appearance deceives would-be predators. Since offspring tend to look like their parents, the survivors produce young which are more likely to survive in their turn. Over millions of years of evolution, under constant pressure from sharp-eyed and hungry predators, many species have produced camouflage which mimics their surroundings, or inedible animals or objects, to an amazing degree.

One Australian spider which spends the day sitting on a leaf looks exactly like a bird-dropping, even spinning a small white web round its black body to complete the illusion. A giant nightjar, the Australian Tawny Frogmouth, becomes a broken branch by day. It sits motionless on a bough, its plumage mimicking the bark of the tree, and the bristly feathers round its mouth representing the splinters where the branch is broken off. The Emperor Moth bears striking eye-spots, which are frightening enough in themselves to an inquisitive bird, but they take on a whole new perspective when the moth is viewed head on. Its round black body and its mottled, eyed wings combine to make it look like the face of a weasel. Two small pink marks near the tip of each wing, irrelevant in the other view, become the inner surface of the weasel's ears, to reinforce the shock. The moth, a day-flier for part of the time, needs only a brief hesitation on the part of the predator to make its escape. Many small birds must also take wing when they see such an apparition.

NATURALLY NOCTURNAL

There is a school of thought which maintains that though the earliest mammals were diurnal, they rapidly adopted nocturnal habits, evolving as they did in the age of the great reptiles. There is, as we shall see, some evidence that the mammalian eye is better designed for a nocturnal existence, with later adaptation for use in daylight. It would make sense that the tiny forerunners of today's mammals should have needed to hide during the day, when agile, predatory reptiles were abroad. The mammals were only able to take over the diurnal niche sixty-five million years ago, when the Age of Reptiles came to an end. However, since only fossils of bony structures of the that period have been found, there is no direct evidence of what the eyes of the earliest mammals might have been like.

THE COOL OF THE NIGHT

Even in temperate regions, the difference in temperature and humidity between night and day can be the difference between life and death for susceptible animals. Thus worms, slugs, frogs, and many lizards must avoid activity during the day, and live mainly in the cool of the night. They must control their body temperature by means of their behaviour, unlike mammals which can do so by physiological means such as sweating.

An intriguing exception to this rule is found in camels, which can be active by day in very hot places without wasting water by sweating. Instead, they store heat in the fatty tissues of their hump during the day, and lose it by radiation during the cold desert night. It is not true that camels store water in their humps, as is so commonly believed; but it is true that they use their humps to save water in this indirect way.

OPPOSITE PAGE
Camels (Camelus dromedarius) *in the Kalahari Desert. Their humps are not full of water, as people used to think, but by storing heat they save water which would otherwise be wasted as sweat.*

Other desert animals, from the smallest insects, scorpions, and spiders to the larger reptiles and mammals, cannot avoid losing water as they breathe – all respiration involves the loss of water – but they are unable readily to replace what they have lost during a normal desert day. Gerbils, jerboas, and other small mammals dig burrows into which they can retreat during the day, and some desert tortoises can burrow deeply into the ground. These excavations are often used by ground squirrels and kangaroo rats, as well as by insects and other small fry.

The very smallest insects cannot burrow, but they can hide during the day in the tunnels of other animals, or in crevices in the rocks. Crickets are among the larger insects which can dig for themselves, though this behaviour will sustain them only from night to night. One of the mealy bugs which lives in South American deserts is able to remain buried during prolonged drought by secreting a waxy covering which is completely waterproof. In this condition, it is able to survive for as long as seventeen years, until water returns and it can resume its nocturnal existence.

Among the other nocturnal inhabitants of arid places are wasps and spiders, which are invisible by day in their burrows, but conduct a complex and often violent night life. Many of the wasps are parasitic on the spiders, laying eggs into their living but paralyzed bodies to provide the wasp larvae with a food supply. Scorpions and solifugids ('camel spiders') also inhabit this dark and dangerous battleground, in which all the combatants are forced to share the night because of their common inability to remain cool and conserve water by any other means.

A THREE-WEEK YEAR

Perhaps the most extraordinary among the animals that burrow to conserve water, emerging only at night, is the Spadefoot Toad, found in some of the driest parts of Arizona, in the United States. It lies buried for eleven months of the year, until the rains fall in July. As little as two and a half millimetres (0.1 in) of rain soaking into the earth will wake it from its sleep, and it digs its way to the surface that night to begin its brief feeding and breeding season. During the first few nights after they emerge, the male toads call loudly and incessantly to attract females to mate with them. When daylight approaches they all retreat below ground to where the sand is moist enough to keep them alive. In the rainy

season, this may be only a couple of centimetres (an inch) under the surface. As the season progresses, the toad must burrow deeper every night, until after about three weeks it resumes its dormant state deep underground.

The Spadefoot Toad's eggs and tadpoles develop very quickly in the temporary pools left by the rain, so that within the same three weeks they have already become tiny adults and burrowed in their turn. During their spell on the surface, many of them succumb to the effects of heat and drought, but once the survivors retreat underground they will never see daylight again.

The Spadefoot Toad survives underground by osmosis, the process by which plants draw water from the soil into their roots. As the toad's blood becomes more concentrated, it draws in through its skin what little water is left in the soil. The concentrated blood also begins to remove water from the contents of the toad's bladder. Thus its permeable skin is the means by which it stays alive during the dry season.

The African bullfrog lives underground in a similar way, but instead of drawing water from the soil, it covers itself in a waterproof coating produced from glands in its skin.

SEEING IN THE DARK

No animal can see in complete darkness. Cave-dwelling fish and salamanders have given up the evolutionary struggle, and saved energy during their development, by having no functional eyes at all. However, where there is a glimmer of light, animals have evolved nocturnal eyes, capable of seeing at very low light intensities.

The first essential is to collect as much light as possible by having a large pupil, but this has drawbacks. The larger the pupil, the bigger the lens must be, and the bigger the lens the more convex it must be to bring the image into focus at the retina, the layer of sensitive cells at the back of the eye. This small bright image can then be enlarged by evolving a bigger eye. There comes a point at which the eyes cannot be any bigger if they are to fit into the head. Here animals diverge according to their place in the nocturnal food chain. Prey animals such as mice sacrifice sharply focussed vision for greater sensitivity, having small eyes but very poor visual acuity, so they can see movements but not sharp images. The largest eyes relative to the size of the animal are those of the Spectral Tarsier, a rat-sized primate living in the East Indies.

TUBULAR EYES

Some predators have evolved oddly-shaped eyes, to retain their acuity without losing sensitivity. The tubular eyes of owls are the classic example of this: the retina is as far from the lens as it would be in a much larger eye, while the middle of the eye is squeezed in to form a tube which will fit within the owl's eye-socket, or orbit. The cornea bulges forward to give the largest possible window on the world. The consequence of this development is that the owl cannot move its eyes within its orbits. To compensate for this immobility, owls have very mobile necks, able to turn through about 270 degrees, though not, as some folk tales would have it, right round to face the front again!

Owls, like many nocturnal predators, are usually short-sighted, but this is not a serious handicap; they do not need to be able to see their prey until it is within striking range.

RODS AND CONES

The retina of a diurnal animal is a mosaic of two types of pigment-filled light-sensitive cells, connected to nerves which transmit signals to the brain. The cells are divided into rods, which respond to the presence or absence of light of all wavelengths, and cones, whose pigments respond selectively to particular wavelengths. In other words, cones can provide the brain with a colour image, while rods 'see' only in black and white. Rods are more sensitive than cones; so truly nocturnal animals have retinas consisting almost entirely of rods, and are unable to see in colour.

Cats and owls, for example, have eyes which are useful by day as well as at night, and they possess a few cones. Experiments have shown that the cones are functional, in the sense that they transmit signals to the brain in response to light of different colours. However, in trials in which the animals are trained to respond to one colour rather than another to get food, cats are failures. Evidently, their brain cannot interpret the signals from the cones, and their vision is effectively monochrome.

A nocturnal retina has many tightly-packed, slender rods, often in more than one layer, connected in groups of several thousand to individual fibres of the optic nerve. This makes for a very sensitive eye, which produces a rather diffuse monochrome image. The sensitivity of such an eye can be increased by having a reflecting layer behind the photosensitive cells. This 'tapetum' makes the most of what little light there is by reflecting it back through the cells to stimulate them a second time. (In a diurnal eye, the light is absorbed by a black pigmented layer at the back.) The tapetum is the cause of the 'eyeshine' of animals seen at night in the headlights of a car, for example.

PINPOINTS, SLITS AND SUNGLASSES

Sensitive eyes need protection from sunlight to prevent the visual pigments from bleaching while the owner is basking in the sun, or running for its life from a diurnal predator. Most animals, except certain strictly nocturnal mammals, can contract their pupils, some to a pinpoint, and some to a slit. Cats can close their pupils almost completely, leaving two tiny holes, one at each end of the slit, to provide a pair of tiny images on the retina. Some nocturnal geckos have four such holes, formed by notches on the inner edge of the iris. When the iris is relaxed at night, their pupil, like that of a cat at night, is round.

All birds have round pupils, whether they are nocturnal or diurnal. But they have a form of protection which is not shared by other animals: the nictitating membrane, or third eyelid, can be drawn across each eye from the side. It acts as a filter in strong light, rather like a pair of sunglasses.

COLOUR-BLIND ANCESTORS?

It is often said that all animals evolved originally to live in the light, and that being nocturnal is a secondary adaptation. If this is true, it must have evolved very early in the history of the mammals. We have seen that cats have eyes which can respond to colour, but lack the brain-power to perceive it. The colour-blindness of bulls is well established, if only as a contradiction to the old saying about the effect on them of a red rag. Rats have a few cones among the rods of their retina, but they are spaced so far apart that they could never form a coloured image. So it begins to look as though mammals are naturally colour-blind, with colour vision as a later evolutionary development, and this in turn suggests that the earliest mammals might have been nocturnal.

The first mammals descended from a group of reptiles known as the synapsids, which died out about 160 million years ago. From then until the late Cretaceous period, 80 million years ago, there are no remains in the fossil record that resemble modern mammals. Where were they all that time? One persuasive answer is that they were small, insectivorous animals, perhaps living in trees, almost certainly nocturnal, and hiding from the dinosaurs, the reptiles which ruled the world until their sudden disappearance at the end of the Cretaceous. If this is anywhere near the truth, it would explain why most mammals are colour-blind, with nocturnal eyes (or at least nocturnal brains) on to which colour vision was grafted as a later development, once the mammals were free to develop along their own line.

Like the chicken and the egg, this is a conundrum which has no answer – or several mutually contradictory answers – but it is nevertheless an intriguing subject for harmless musing.

OPPOSITE PAGE
*A cat's eyes are nocturnal. To protect the sensitive retina in bright light, the cat (*Felis domesticus*) can close its pupils to slits. Through the small remaining gap, it can keep an eye on its surroundings.*

EARS IN THE NIGHT

When vision is not enough to give an animal a full picture of its surroundings, it must rely on information from other senses. Hearing is the most useful sense for many nocturnal animals, both predator and prey. With few exceptions, nocturnal animals do not have specialized hearing – just sharper ears and a quicker response to the information they convey.

Evolution has played its part in the parallel development of predator and prey in the accoustic realm as well as in other ways. It is not a coincidence, for example, that mice communicate with each other at a very high frequency, about 100 kilohertz, and that the hearing range of cats and owls, while it is very high by human standards, runs out beyond about 10 kilohertz.

LISTENING FOR DANGER

The importance of sound to rabbits, prey animals par excellence, is illustrated by an old country weather prediction: that to see rabbits feeding by day is a sign of wet weather. In fact, it is more likely to be a sign that it is raining already, or that it rained the previous night. Rabbits depend upon their hearing while they are feeding at night, to warn them of the approach of predators; if it is raining heavily, they cannot hear warning noises. In wet weather, they stay underground at night, coming out to feed only when daylight allows them to keep watch for danger.

A prey animal needs not only to be able to detect noises, but also to locate their source. This is why deer and rabbits, antelope and many other prey animals have large mobile outer ears, which can swivel to locate sounds. Direction-finding ability is even more important for predators.

SOUND LOCATION

Humans were once thought to be the best animals at locating sounds, using stereophonic hearing to judge the tiny difference in time between the arrival of a sound at each ear. From this information, together with the way in which sounds from one side are blocked by the head from reaching the opposite ear, the brain rapidly calculates the direction from which the sound must have come. Today, it is known that cats are much better than humans at locating sounds, as befits their status as predators. The sequence of senses used by a cat during an attack is first hearing, then smell, then vision, and often in the final moments touch, as its whiskers guide its teeth to cut off the prey animal's final lunge for freedom.

OWLS AND BATS: PRECISION HEARING

The real experts at direction-finding by sound are owls and bats, which are both highly specialized for the task. Owls are celebrated for their silent flight. Their wings and body are covered with soft feathers which not only deaden the sound of the owl's flight so that the prey cannot hear it coming, but also enable the owl to hear better the movements of its prey.

The direction-finding ability of an owl arises from its expert use of stereophonic hearing, like a human. In locating sounds in the horizontal plane, and deciding whether they are coming from left, right, or centre, an owl is as good as a human. However, it excels where human beings fail, at determining the elevation of a sound, that is, its position in the vertical plane. It can do this because of the asymmetrical position of its ears. Most owls' right ears face slightly upwards, and the left ears downwards by about the same amount. In the vertical plane, the bird responds to high-frequency sounds, like the rustle of leaves or the scratch of small claws on a log. As the source of sound moves downwards, the owl hears it more loudly in the left ear, and less loudly in the right. When it moves upwards, the opposite happens. Thus owls can pinpoint sounds in both planes with great accuracy.

It is said that a Barn Owl can locate and catch a running mouse in total darkness – even knowing in which direction it is moving so that it can catch it in its talons from the side – by the use of its remarkable sense of hearing. All this is done by hearing the *movements* of the mouse – not its squeaks, which are at too high a frequency.

ECHOES IN THE NIGHT

Bats obtain their view of the world by echo-location. In principal this is a very simple system: the bat makes a short, sharp sound, and listens for its echo. The time the echo takes to return to the bat's ear tells the bat how far away an obstacle is. The quality of the echo also contains some information about the texture and size of the obstacle, and the bat's stereophonic hearing enables it to locate the source of the echo.

In practice, the amount of information that has to be processed, and the speed at which the bat interprets it, is staggering. The bat is able to make decisions and act on them while it is in flight, often at high speed, in pursuit of a flying insect. The jinking, darting flight of bats at dusk, like dead leaves in a gale, may look random, but every twist and turn is under full control, and ends with another small meal safely in the bat's mouth. Little Brown Bats in the United States can catch mosquitoes and fruit flies at the rate of two per second.

Such an amazing ability has naturally attracted the attention of researchers, especially now that electronics has reached the stage where recording and interpreting the bat's echo-location sounds is relatively simple. The results have increased human respect for the intricacy and accuracy of the system.

The pulses are very short, between 5 and 15 milliseconds long, and very high-pitched, between 20 and 120 kilohertz. This is beyond the hearing range of nearly all humans, though a few young children can hear the bats' lower frequencies. The short duration of the pulse allows the bat time to listen

OPPOSITE PAGE
Mexican Free-tailed Bats (Tadarida brasiliensis) *stream out of Bracken Cave, Texas, USA. The colony, with thirty million members, is the largest gathering of warm-blooded animals on earth.*

for the echo and determine its timing exactly; and the high frequency is well above that of other natural sounds, which reduces the risk of interference. Scientists testing this last hypothesis subjected flying bats to artificial sounds within their frequency range, and found that the bats quickly became disorientated.

Bats produce their sounds with a modified larynx, and direct them by using their lips, or specialized structures round the nostrils which can look bizarre to human eyes. They receive the echoes with large, often complex, external ears, which guide the sound to sensitive internal ears. The bats are not deafened by the loud sounds they make because, as each sound is produced, tiny muscles reduce the sensitivity of the inner ear for exactly the right period of time.

There are many technical accounts of bat echo-location, brimming with astonishing information, which are worth looking up in a library. Here, there is only space to record one such piece of gee-whizzardry. A Horseshoe Bat with a wingspan of 40 cm (16 ins) was able to fold its wings and fly through a net composed of 14 cm (5½ ins) squares, made of transparent nylon threads 80 micromillimetres (.003 ins) thick. It did this without touching the sides, and in total darkness. Compared with such precision, vision seems a crude and inaccurate sense.

OTHER ECHO-LOCATORS

Although they are not nocturnal animals, dolphins, including killer whales, use their own very precise form of echo-location, sending out sound pulses which are focussed by the domed, oil-filled 'forehead' and the concave shape of the front of the skull. The returning echoes are received at the point of the lower jaw, from where they are transmitted to the ear along oil-filled canals. It is said that the echo-location system of a killer whale is precise enough to distinguish between a cod and the much preferred salmon at fifty metres.

Echo-location of a much simpler kind is used by shrews, and by birds which nest in caves. Cave swiftlets change their calls from a normal social twittering outside the cave to a deeper, buzzing echo-location sound, easily heard by humans, as they pass through the entrance.

If you move about in a dark, unfamiliar room, you are nonetheless aware of the presence of some unseen obstacles. Usually this works only at close range, and at or near head height, preventing collisions with a wall-cupboard, perhaps,

or the wall itself. This is a very crude form of echo-location, in which the ears, their sensitivity heightened in the dark, pick up faint echoes of one's own movements, or even the sound of one's own breathing. However, compared with bats, we are helpless in the dark.

NOSING ABOUT

For nocturnal animals, a good sense of smell is an asset whether they are prey or predator. The scent of a lion or a fox, borne on the breeze, is enough to alert an antelope or a rabbit, preparing them for flight when another warning, perhaps a small sound, triggers the reaction. The lion or the fox may well be sniffing the breeze themselves, in search of their next meal.

The sense of smell involves taking and testing a sample of the environment with chemoreceptors, which respond differently to different molecules. Smell is usually differentiated from the sense of taste, though both work in a very similar way; smell checks a sample of air drawn into the nostrils, while taste checks a sample of solid or liquid from the surroundings, usually in the mouth. Many insects, such as flies and butterflies, have chemoreceptors in their feet, and they use these to test potential food, or find places to lay their eggs.

Snakes and lizards have a few chemosensory cells in their nostrils, but their sense of smell depends in the main on a second set of chemoreceptors, in addition to the 'normal' system, of which they seem to make little use. The forked tips of their flickering tongues collect samples, either from the air or from the substrate, and transfer them to two hollows inside the front of the upper jaw. These, the Jacobson's organs, are lined with sensory cells which enable the animal to identify the molecules it has collected.

LONG AND SHORT RANGE SMELLING

For many animals, scent can work at quite long range. Male moths, using their branching antennae to sample the air, fly along a scent gradient from weaker to stronger, until they find a female emitting the attractive aroma of their species. Dung beetles can detect the scent of their food in the air from several kilometres away in good conditions.

However, most animals that sniff out their food do so at close quarters, following a gradient in the same way, but on a much smaller scale. The image of the bloodhound, nose to the ground in pursuit of a villain, is familiar; but small rodents, hedgehogs, cats and mongooses – and even some birds – seek food in the same way.

The idea of birds having a sense of smell seems odd, because they are such obviously visual creatures. A blindfolded bird will not take to the air, though it will fly in self-preservation if it is thrown aloft, and it will have great difficulty in landing. Birds possess a full set of olfactory organs, but with a few exceptions, seem not to use them. Among these exceptions are two nocturnal species from New Zealand, which have evolved to fill niches that are vacant because the islands originally had no mammals, apart from a couple of species of bats.

The Kiwi is a flightless bird, secretive and nocturnal in its habits, which was not noticed until forty years after the first Europeans arrived in New Zealand. It has a long, flexible bill, with the nostril openings at the tip, a condition found in no other bird. It has very small eyes, suggesting that sight is unimportant to it, and though its large ear-apertures suggest a good sense of hearing, its principal means of finding food is by smell. It snuffles through the leaf litter in search of insects and earthworms as if it were an insectivorous mammal. It will also take fallen berries when it can find them.

The other scent-led bird in New Zealand is the Kakapo, or 'owl-parrot'. It is a flightless nocturnal parrot which looks rather like an owl, having a facial disc made up of radiating feathers round its eyes. It is mainly vegetarian, feeding on grasses, mosses and fruits, but also on flowers, which it locates by their scent. It occasionally eats lizards, though it probably catches them more by chance than because of any specialized hunting technique. The only other bird that is known to find its food at night by scent is the oilbird, which feeds on ripe fruits, chiefly from palms, or plants of the laurel family.

A FOREST MAINTAINED AT NIGHT

The sense of smell of two small mammals is an important link in the chain that supports the once-vast ancient coniferous rainforests of the western United States. These forests once stretched unbroken from California to Alaska, but only about 13 per cent of them remains, after a century of intensive logging. Where areas of sufficient size survive, for example in Olympic National Park in western Washington State, they illustrate how delicate such a huge ecosystem can be.

Rainforests are aptly described as 'trees standing on a desert'. They depend very little on the geological substrate beneath them, but are instead largely self-supporting, growing in a soil which is composed of debris falling from the trees themselves, their own dead fallen trunks, and allied plants such as ferns and lichens. In the well-drained gravelly soils on which they grow, the massive rainfall (about 4 m (12 ft) per year) would wash these nutrients away, but for a system of mycorrhizal fungi, a network of millions of tiny filaments wrapped round the roots of all the trees. The fungal filaments retain water and minerals, and pass them to the tree roots, taking in return some of the sugar made by the trees, which the fungi cannot make for themselves. They produce fruit-bodies underground (gourmets know them as truffles) and they depend on some outside agency to disperse their spores. This agency is a group of nocturnal mammals.

There are over one hundred different species of truffles, each producing highly-scented fruit bodies. Deer mice and flying squirrels search the forest floor at night to sniff out and dig up the aromatic truffles, which are one of their main sources of food. The spores survive passage through the mammals' digestive systems, and are spread round the forest in their droppings. Without the mammals to disperse them, the fungi would be slow to colonize new tree-roots, and the forest would suffer.

The mice and squirrels are the main prey of the Spotted Owl, a species that is endangered because of the reduction of its habitat. In what is left of the forest, the well-being of the owl is a sign that the mammals are still flourishing, and therefore that the forest itself is still being supplied at night with the fungi essential to its continued survival.

STRANGE SENSES

If part of humanity's general fear of the dark stems from the ability of nocturnal animals to move freely at a time when we are virtually helpless, the most awe-inspiring of those animals are the ones which can use senses that we lack. The heat-seeking ability of pit vipers is an extreme case.

HEAT-SEEKING HUNTERS

Pit vipers get their name from a pair of organs situated below and in front of their eyes. Two deep hollows are each lined with a thin membrane which has a tiny hole in the centre. The membrane contains sensory receptors which can detect infrared radiation, that is, energy at wavelengths so long that humans cannot possibly see it, and yet not long enough for us to perceive it as heat. However, the pit vipers are so sensitive to this radiation that they can detect differences of as little as 0.2°C (.36°F).

The image of the prey that the pit viper sees was left to the imagination until the 'Thermavision' camera was invented, originally as a means of testing the insulation of stoves. Photographs of animals taken with this camera revealed that, however well-insulated they may be, there is always a difference between them and the background, even if only in exposed areas such as nostrils and the inside of their ears. This difference is enough for the pit viper to locate its prey. Because the pit organs are forward-looking, the snake obtains a steroscopic image of the prey animal, from which it can judge its range as it prepares to strike.

SUDDEN DEATH

Pit vipers are among the most venomous of all snakes. They range in size from the Bushmaster, which can grow to over 3 m (9½ ft) long, to the tiny Fer-de-lance, which may be less than 10 cm (4 ins). They are found in all the warmer regions of the world except Africa. As well as ground-living forms such as the Bushmaster and the Fer-de-lance, there is a group which lives in trees, the largest of which, *Trimeresurus trigonocephalus*, over 1 m (3 ft) long, lives in the Nicobar Islands in the Bay of Bengal. Moccasins frequent swamps in the southern United States and Central America. The Himalayan pit viper lives at up to 5,000 m (16,000 ft), the greatest altitude of any snake in the world. The desert-dwelling rattlesnakes, including the sidewinder, are probably the best known pit vipers, because of the impression they made on the early European explorers of North America.

All pit vipers possess powerful venom, which is produced from enlarged venom glands, housed in the typical diamond-shaped head, and delivered through fangs which are too long to fit inside their closed mouths. To overcome this, the fangs are folded back against the roof of the snake's mouth until they are brought into action, when they swing forward as the snake strikes. The whole system is designed to drop a victim at the first bite, presumably to save the snake having to renew the hunt for its rapidly-cooling prey in the darkness of the desert night.

ELECTRIC FISH

Several species of fish use electricity, some as a weapon, and others as a means of perceiving their surroundings. Strongly electric fish such as electric eels and electric rays can produce shocks which are enough to stun their prey, but they are not capable of receiving and interpreting electric stimuli. Dogfish and other sharks are able to find a prey animal by sensing the disturbance which it causes to the earth's magnetic field, even when it is buried under several centimetres of sand on the dark sea bed, but they do not produce electricity of their own. Two families, the Mormyrids of tropical Africa and the Gymnotid eels of South and Central America, known as the 'weakly electric' fish, can generate electricity *and* detect changes in the field they have created, caused by their surroundings. These fish are all nocturnal, and live in muddy rivers, where it is impossible to see.

The electric organs are modified muscles, modified only in scale, since the nerve-muscle link is already electrical. They produce a discharge which pulses at up to 300 times per second, and they are able to monitor the changes produced in this fluctuating field by means of receptors distributed over their skin. The receptors are divided into two types, analogous to the rods and cones of the eye. One type responds to rapid changes in the field, and the other to slow changes, though not all species have both types. In this way they can distinguish between good and bad conductors in their immediate vicinity. Evidently they can then interpret this information in terms of what is edible, and what should be avoided, though the sense is so alien to us humans that it is hard to imagine what it must feel like to the fish! However it works, the weak electrical field is also used by the fishes to communicate with each other, by sending and receiving electrical pulses in their turbid, dark environment.

MESSAGES IN THE NIGHT

All animals use whatever senses they have to communicate with each other at some level. Electric fish recognize the fields produced by others of their kind, and respond appropriately, either by deliberately showing themselves, or by altering their pulse-rate so that the interference between the two fields is reduced, whereupon they must effectively disappear as far as the other fish is concerned.

Butterflies and moths are able to see ultra-violet light, which is invisible to humans. They have made use of this ability in their evolution: the only characteristic separating several pairs of otherwise very similar species is the ultra-

violet patterns on their wings. Incidentally – but inevitably – flowers that are pollinated by butterflies, and other insects such as bees and hoverflies which share the ability to see ultra-violet, bear ultra-violet markings which attract the insects and direct them to the source of nectar.

Moths are among the many insects that are attracted by the ultra-violet component in the light from mercury vapour lamps, though it is hard to understand why they should be: one would expect nocturnal insects to keep away from light. However, there are some nocturnal animals, including insects, which use visual signals to communicate in the dark.

FLASHES OF INSPIRATION

In the dark, light is a rare but very useful means of signalling among animals which are able to produce it. Conspicuous among such bioluminescent animals are the glowworms or fireflies. These nocturnal beetles produce light whose colour and pattern of long or short flashes, at greater or lesser intervals, distinguishes the species. In areas where several species coexist, this distinction by a type of moving morse code is important in saving time and energy. It is also very beautiful to the human eye. Usually, the female perches on a grass blade, or low in a bush, unilluminated until a male flies by, emitting the flashing signal which shows that he is of her own species. She responds with a matching code, which causes him to fly down to mate with her. Thus females save energy by not flashing until it is necessary, and males do not waste time courting females of a species other than their own.

However, there is one firefly in Florida which has turned this signalling system to its own nefarious purposes. The female of this large, predatory species waits for a male – any male – to fly over, and then mimics the signal that he is producing. When he flies down to mate with her, she waits for him to come within range, and then eats him. Only males of her own species, emitting their own specific signal, are allowed to mate unmolested, though there is some suggestion that they, too, may become grist to her mill once that task is accomplished. This intriguing story emerged when it was discovered that male fireflies will fly down to flashes from a simple hand-held torch, if their own code is imitated accurately enough. Patient observation revealed that predatory females were visited by males of several different species, indicating that they had mastered the art of imitation many millions of years before the scientists.

Many species of deep-water fish produce light. Some of the lantern fish have an illuminated lure dangling above their mouth, like a lantern on a pole, to attract curious fish, which become their prey. Others, like the Hatchet Fish, use light organs on their lower surface as a form of camouflage, breaking up or concealing completely their silhouette, seen from below against the slightly lighter water above. Several species of the genus *Anomalops* are able to flash their lights by means of covers, rather like eyelids, over the light-producing organs, and there is every reason to suppose that this is a form of signalling, though so far its significance is a mystery.

NOISES IN THE NIGHT

Sound is by far the commonest means of communication among nocturnal animals. The calls of owls are an important part of the mysterious atmosphere of the night, wandering disembodied voices that raise the hackles on human necks. The song of the Nightingale, on the other hand, raises the spirits of human hearers. A Nightingale's song is remarkable for its variety and tone, which might be thought unnecessary at night, in the absence of competition from other singing species. However, the mystery is easily solved: Nightingales also sing by day, when their songs need to be readily distinguished from those of other vocal artists of the bird world, such as thrushes and blackbirds.

Many primates communicate at night by long, loud calls. Gibbons produce complex songs which are audible over great distances in the forest; Howler monkeys make a low roaring noise which has been likened to the sound of a distant waterfall. Both species call intermittently during the day, but at night the calls are more important, perhaps as a form of reassurance as one group confirms the presence of another nearby. The beautiful calls of the Indris, one of Madagascar's many endangered species of lemur, blend in weird harmony in the forest as members of a tribe out of sight of each other maintain contact over a considerable distance in the darkness.

OPPOSITE PAGE
A female Black Howler Monkey (Alovatta caraya) *at Gran Chaco in Argentina. Groups of howler monkeys call to warn other groups of their presence. The calls of a group can carry as far as 5 km (3 miles) on a still night.*

VOCAL BATTLES

Vocalization may serve a different purpose when groups of certain primates move too close together. In this case, calls may be used to establish territorial boundaries. Often two groups of chimpanzees or colobus monkeys will indulge in a vocal contest, indicating to each other the size and strength of their party, while avoiding the risk of injury inherent in physical conflict between rival tribes. Within a tribe, the power of an individual's voice often determines its position in the group, the highest rank being held by the owner of the loudest voice.

Male orang-utans, in the remaining forests of Borneo and Sumatra, make a loud vocal demonstration from time to time. This 'long call' begins when they break off a branch and hurl it to the ground. Next, they emit a series of loud roars, rising to an ear-splitting bellow, before falling quiet. The whole call may last two minutes. In the relative silence that follows, they listen for replies from other males nearby. The 'long call' is almost certainly a warning to nearby males on the verge of infringing the caller's territory.

Several species have evolved adaptations to increase their voice-power, improving their chances of ruling the roost and mating with the most and choicest females. Howler monkeys have an enlarged lower jaw and hyoid bone which increases the power of their calls. The Douroucouli, or night monkey, has a very loud voice for such a small animal, because of an inflatable sac beneath its chin which functions as a resonator.

WOLF MUSIC

Wolves and jackals, coyotes, and other members of the dog family, also communicate at night, by howling. The drawn-out, high-pitched calls can be heard a long distance away, as the animals announce their presence and listen for the voices of others. No two wolves call in the same way. Their calls sound distinct even to human ears, and they are certainly used by wolves to identify themselves to members of their own pack.

Detailed studies of wolf calls have shown that they are not simple notes, but contain overtones (harmonics) which stimulate other wolves nearby to howl as well. Some wolves have better voices than others, both in terms of their power and of the richness of the harmonics they can produce. Most have a vocal range of less than an octave, but some can exceed

this, to produce one of the eeriest and most haunting sounds in nature.

The effect of the harmonics can be mimicked by blowing a mouth-organ within earshot of a domestic dog; in many cases, the reedy sound of the instrument, full of harmonics, stimulates some ancestral canine memory, and sets the dog howling.

SINGERS AND SILENTS

On the vast grasslands of Texas, the characteristic sound of a warm summer night was once the song of millions of crickets. Now, sadly, the most common sound is the rush of traffic on the highways or the drone of aircraft overhead. Crop sprays have done great damage to the cricket populations, but along road-edges and in a few protected places the crickets still survive, to sing through the night.

Safe in the dark from the attentions of insect-eating birds, males of each species chirp or buzz or rattle to attract females to mate with them. The females select the males with the loudest voices. To the crickets, the noise of the traffic is unimportant. Each female is sensitive only to the range of tones produced by her own species. The males, too, can hear each other; they respond by spreading out, so that their own call is not confused with that of their neighbours. These miniature territories are jealously protected; calling males are frequently involved in fights when one invades another's calling ground.

Thus calling has its price. Although it attracts females, it may also be the cause of fights with rivals, which may be more powerful. It has another, more grisly, consequence: there is a species of nocturnal parasitic fly which homes in on the calls of male crickets, to deposit a larva on their abdomens. The larva penetrates the cricket's skin, and feeds on its body, eventually killing it.

Some males have evolved a defence against the violent jealousy of other males, and against the parasitic fly. They visit the breeding grounds, but they do not call at all. They hang around silently near to a male which is in good voice, waiting for a female to approach. When the female arrives, the silent male gives a small, surreptitious chirrup, and mates with her.

The success at breeding of the two types is about equal. Calling males probably get more mates, but they are involved in more fights and attract the attention of parasitic flies. Silent males, by avoiding the danger, live longer and have an equal number of opportunities of mating.

IT'S A FROG'S LIFE

We have already seen the importance of calling to Spadefoot Toads, during their brief annual sojourn above ground in Arizona. In the rainforests of Central America, which contain some of the world's densest and most varied populations of frogs, calling at night in the breeding season is vital, so that females can find males of their own species.

As with the crickets in Texas, each female responds only to the calls of her own kind. The calls vary in pitch and rhythm, from the low croaking of bullfrogs to the high, abrupt chirruping of the smallest tree-frogs. Many species have air-sacs which they inflate as they call, and these act as resonators. The resulting choral cacophony can be deafening to humans, but to each species of frog it must sound like a series of siren songs of its own species, a solo invitation to fertilization.

OPPOSITE PAGE

A Coyote (Canis latrans) *in the Sonoran desert, in California. The main food of coyotes is rodents and rabbits, which they hunt day and night. Their musical howls are a characteristic sound of the desert night.*

Such a dense mass of food attracts predators, especially snakes, which glide through the night in search of something to eat. All snakes are deaf, so the calls are no guide to the whereabouts of their prey. But the snakes have their Jacobson's organs to show them where the air contains the most molecules of frog-scent, and they are very successful predators. Some eat the frogs themselves, and others specialize in eating the masses of tree frog eggs that accumulate on the leaves and twigs of the breeding area.

SCENT IN THE NIGHT

Male moths have branching antennae to guide them along scent gradients to where females of their species are pumping out pheromones, or aerial hormones, into the night. These pheromones are sometimes used by farmers as species-specific bait to attract moths which are pests, removing them from circulation at mating time when they are especially susceptible to the lure of female scent.

The most extreme example of this long-distance attraction is the Vapourer Moth, a species in which the female is flightless. When the eggs hatch, the caterpillars undertake a massive migration, walking as much as two kilometres in search of a suitable tree on which to pupate, feeding as they go. When they are fully grown, each attaches itself to the trunk of the chosen tree and spins a cocoon. When the adults emerge, the males are free-flying.

The female does not move from the spot. Instead, she grips the cocoon and begins to pump out pheromone. The scent drifts downwind, still effective over a kilometre away. Males pick it up and fly from weaker to stronger concentrations until they find and mate with the female. Neither sex feeds during its short adult life; they do not even possess the proboscis that they would need to feed. Each exists only to reproduce, using the energy they gathered as caterpillars.

OPPOSITE PAGE
Common Frogs (Rana temporaria), *like most amphibians, are active mainly at night. Although they have lungs, they absorb half the oxygen they need through their skin, which must remain moist. One of their main food items is earthworms, which are also active at night.*

Moths with this type of life-cycle may be compared to the flowers on plants, the brief, purely sexual phase of a life, most of which is sexless.

Amphibians are mostly nocturnal, and need moisture to stop their skin from drying out. Although frogs have lungs, they get at least half their oxygen supply through their skin, which must remain moist for the purpose. Salamanders have no lungs, and must breathe entirely through their skin and the lining of their mouths. Several species live their whole lives in caves, never metamorphosing into adults; some of these are blind and colourless, save for the bright red of their gills. They are able to breed in the larval state, but how they find each other in total darkness was a puzzle for a long time, because they seem to have so few senses.

All salamanders lack ears, though they are not completely deaf. They can respond to airborne sounds, but only those below 244 cycles (about the same pitch as the 'mains hum' on faulty audio equipment), which they perceive through their bodies as vibrations. Most of them, the cave-dwellers in particular, need to be in close contact with their surroundings, becoming agitated and disorientated if they drift away from a rock in a pool, for example.

Apart from touch, a salamander's main sense is either taste or smell (the two are closely linked in amphibians, as they are in reptiles). The cells inside their nostrils, and their Jacobson's organs, are highly developed. They communicate during the breeding season by means of scent, produced from a gland on the chin of the male as a sticky discharge. The scent appears to attract fertile females through the silent, lightless crawling space that is the salamander's world.

BIRDS OF THE NIGHT

Birds are such obviously visual, and therefore apparently diurnal, animals that the nocturnal species seem very odd to us. The Nightingale, with its rich and beautiful song, seems out of place among the other sounds of the night. Where owls and nightjars produce calls designed to carry well through woodland or across meadows, or corncrakes produce monotonous scratching calls which are hard for a predator to locate, the Nightingale advertizes its presence with a song which does not carry very far, but is easy to pin down. Its safety from foxes depends on the fact that it sings from deep within a bush, where even the hungriest predator would find it difficult to catch.

There are three main groups of birds that are adapted for nocturnal life: the owls and the Kiwi, which we have already met, and the oilbird. Nightjars are, strictly speaking, crepuscular, though they can feed on bright moonlit nights. Some seabirds, particularly petrels and shearwaters, come to land only during the breeding season and then only at night, when they show great skill in finding their nests in darkness. It is said that they locate their own burrow among many by its individual smell. Although they feed mainly by day far out at sea for most of the year, they show some adaptations to their nocturnal activity during the breeding season: for example, the retina of a Manx Shearwater contains more rods than that of a Fulmar, a petrel which breeds on cliffs, and comes ashore during the day.

Wading birds often have no choice but to feed at night, since their feeding-grounds may be accessible only at low tide. They show no particular adaptations to nocturnal life; their alert behaviour, and readiness to fly at the approach of danger are the same by day and by night. They are not in particular danger from predators even when they cannot see them coming: if the mudflats or sandbanks where they feed at low tide are not cut off from the shore by channels of water, they are still too soft to take the weight of even a small carnivore.

THE MYSTERIOUS OILBIRD

The oilbird is related to the nightjar, though it has some characteristics which make it seem more like an owl. Its behaviour and ecology are unique. oilbirds get their name from their enormous chicks, which are very fat. They live in colonies in caves, in Central America and the West Indies. An oilbird roosts by day, crouching on a ledge, and flies out to feed at night. It has a powerful hooked bill rather like that of a hawk, but it does not use it to kill or dismember its prey. It feeds on fruits, mainly those of the oil-nut palm, using its bill to pluck them on the wing. It returns to the cave towards dawn, to digest the food which it has crammed into its stomach during the night. It regurgitates the seeds, dropping them on to the cave floor, where they germinate in a rich bed of droppings. In the absence of light, the seedlings become etiolated and die.

The fruits which oilbirds eat are often spicy or aromatic, and it is widely believed that they find their food by the smell. They have large eyes, however, and probably navigate outside the cave by sight. Inside, they find their way round the cave systems by echo-location calls, clicking and buzzing like cave swiftlets.

TALONS IN THE DUSK

Although it is not strictly nocturnal, one bird of prey deserves inclusion here: the Bat Hawk which lives in Africa and parts of the Far East. As its name suggests, it feeds mainly on bats. It hunts at dusk, when the bats are streaming out of their daytime roosts, feeding voraciously for about half an hour, until its prey has dispersed and is too hard to catch. It has large eyes, and a very wide mouth, rather like that of the nightjar. It swallows its prey in flight, no doubt to avoid wasting good hunting time by stopping to dismember it. It also takes swallows and martins, as they fly in to their roosts.

OPPOSITE PAGE
A Barn Owl (Tyto alba) *sets out to hunt at sunset. It has specially adapted tubular eyes for vision in dim light, but it catches its prey mainly by hearing.*

The Bat Hawk needs a large open space over which to hunt, because it is so big and flies so fast that hunting in woodland would be dangerous. A pool or a mangrove creek are ideal, and football fields and town squares are popular. Travellers used to tell of the excitement of seeing a Bat Hawk hunting over the platforms of Makindu railway station, in Kenya, taking the bats as they emerged from the station roof.

TRAVELLERS IN THE NIGHT

Many small birds migrate by night, because of the danger from diurnal birds of prey along their route. There has been a long debate about how they manage to find their way, with a number of suggestions being put forward and tested. It now seems that diurnal birds, ranging from songbirds to buzzards, use a combination of cues to navigate across continents and oceans in the dark.

It was suggested early on that they navigate in the same way as human seafarers, by observing the position of the stars. This idea was at first mockingly rejected, on the grounds that for many centuries humans were unable to use anything but the Pole Star, which remains stationary, until they had invented a reliable chronometer by which to predict the positions of the other stars as the constellations revolve during the night. Later, experiments were done in planetaria, rotating the sky above a cage full of birds and watching their reactions. Sure enough, the birds gathered on the side of the cage nearest to the direction in which they would normally fly, as indicated by the artificial sky above them. It appears that they have an internal chronometer as accurate as anything made by humans.

On cloudy nights, when the stars are not visible, the birds still manage to find their way. Tiny magnetic caps fitted to migrating birds have shown that they are sensitive to the earth's magnetic field, and are able to orient themselves from its mainly north-south direction. If the magnets in the caps are too strong, the birds become disorientated; if the fields surrounding them are altered, the birds alter their choice of direction accordingly.

Experiments with groups of students, transported blindfold across country in buses and then invited to point in the direction of their starting-place, have shown that this magnetic sense is found to some small extent in humans. Students who were given hats containing small magnets were significantly less successful at direction-finding than those wearing the same hats without the magnets, some of whom were surprisingly accurate.

LOST SENSES – OR UNDEVELOPED POTENTIAL?

The existence of the magnetic sense and the crude echo-location abilities found in humans, together with the heightened senses of hearing and smell noticed in blind people, suggest that we possess the basic equipment to take up a nocturnal existence. With the exception of the infra-red ability of the pit vipers, or the electric sense of certain fish, humans are possessed of all the senses they would need to live in the dark. It is common to bemoan our loss of sensitivity, as if living in the modern world had somehow coarsened us; but in fact it is our superb vision that has made our other senses relatively dull, because they are relatively redundant.

In the case of smell, for example, our position is rather like that of the cat whose eyes can see colour but whose brain cannot perceive it. Our sense of smell is famously evocative, so that one whiff of modelling clay sends our memories back to our schooldays, or the smell of linseed oil can send a cricketer into a trance. We can distinguish between a multiplicity of aromas if we have to; and those who do have to, such as perfume-blenders or wine-tasters, demonstrate a potential that is there to be trained. What is lacking is the vocabulary with which to understand the information that our sense of smell brings us every minute of the day.

Musicians, similarly, show the subtlety of our sense of hearing. However, they have a vocabulary, and even a method of writing, with which to express at least the areas which interest them, such as pitch and tone.

Perhaps our fascination with the animals of the night is not so much because their lives are alien to our own, as because they are only just beyond our reach.

OPPOSITE PAGE
An Elephant Hawk Moth (Deilephila elpenor) *seeks out honeysuckle at night, to feed on the nectar. During the day, its pinkish-green wings serve as camouflage, hiding it from predators on its larval food plant, rosebay willow herb.*

SAFETY IN THE DARK

Nocturnal animals use the night as cover. They may be hiding from predators, or from the effects of heat and sunlight, or from their prey, the better to catch it. For many of them, the other side of the nocturnal coin is the need to be able to hide in daylight.

OPPOSITE PAGE

*Moving at night can be dangerous in today's world. Common Toads (*Bufo bufo*) migrate in spring to their breeding ponds, often crossing roads to reach them.*

Hippos (Hippopotamus amphibius) *are usually active at night, though they spend part of each day basking in the sun. They are sensitive to over-heating, and to sunburn.*

RIGHT *The Leaf-tailed Gecko* (Phyllurus cornutus) *is a good example of daytime camouflage in a nocturnal animal. By pressing its body close to a tree-trunk, it reduces the shadows which would give it away to a predator.*

Geckos (Gekko vittatus), *like this one from the Solomon Islands, have soft skin, with many tiny scales. Because the scales do not overlap, a gecko's skin is not waterproof: it must therefore avoid direct sunlight. Most geckos are nocturnal for this reason.*

LEFT *The Great Grey Slug* (Limax maximus), *like most molluscs, must remain cool and damp, which means that it must hide during the day. It lays its eggs in dark, damp places where they are safe from the drying effects of sun and air.*

*Nightjars are found all over the world, perfectly camouflaged to hide during the day. This is a European Nightjar (*Caprimulgus europaeus).

LEFT ABOVE *The Dwarf Puff Adder (*Bitis peringueyi) *in Namibia spends the heat of the day buried in the sand. But in the early morning it is often seen on the surface.*

LEFT BELOW *Kangaroo Rats (*Dipodomys deserti) *spend the day in burrows in sandy soil, but at night may travel great distances to find food.*

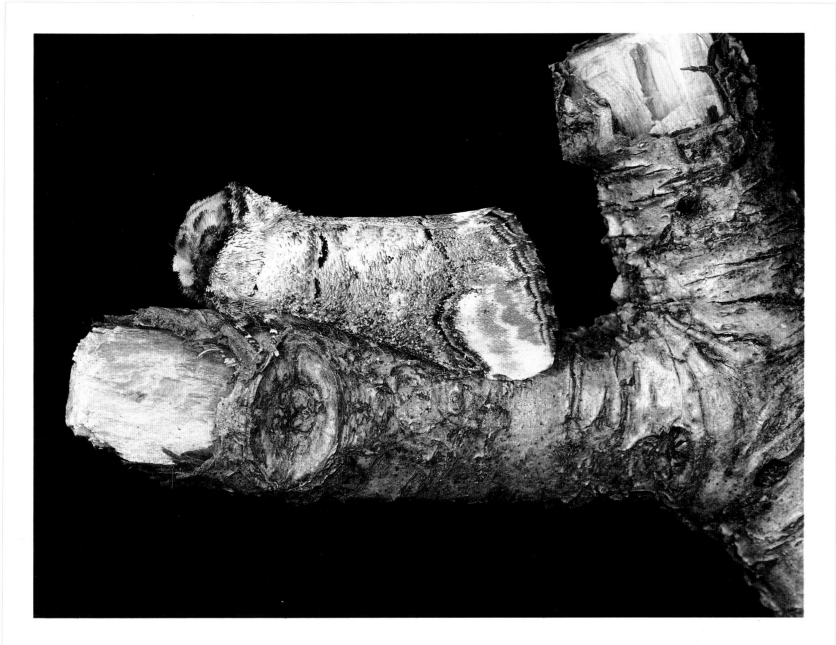

A Buff-tip Moth (Phalera bucephala) *is a perfect mimic of a broken twig, in this case a dead oak twig on the woodland floor.*

LEFT *A Tawny Frogmouth* (Podargus strigoides) *in Queensland, Australia, when alarmed, adopts a 'broken branch' posture. Frogmouths are active at dusk and dawn. Although they are related to nightjars, they feed by pouncing on prey on the ground, not catching it on the wing.*

*With flattened body and legs, centipedes (*Scolopendra
cingulatus) *are well adapted for hunting in leaf litter, searching
out creatures which might be hiding from other predators
during the day.*

*A Solifugid (*Solifuga solpuga*), sometimes called a wind scorpion, sun spider, or camel spider, is a very successful nocturnal hunter of insects, spiders, and even mice. Running swiftly, it holds its front legs out as feelers, though it also has a well-developed pair of eyes.*

A male Emperor Moth (Saturnia pavonia) *flies by day as well as at night, but its camouflage is designed for when it is immobile in daylight. Bright eyespots on its wings are augmented by pink 'ears', which together with its black body make it look like the face of a small mammal.*

RIGHT *The Mottled Beauty Moth* (Alcis repandata) *is found all across northern and central Europe, and into Asia. It lives mainly in pine forests, and adults may vary in colour from pale to nearly black, depending on the type of forest in which they were hatched.*

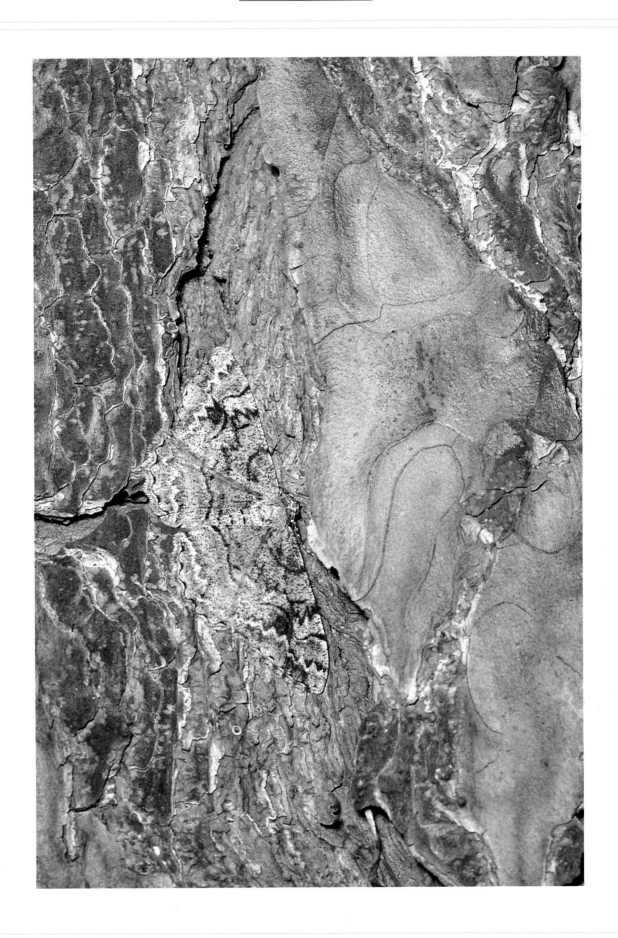

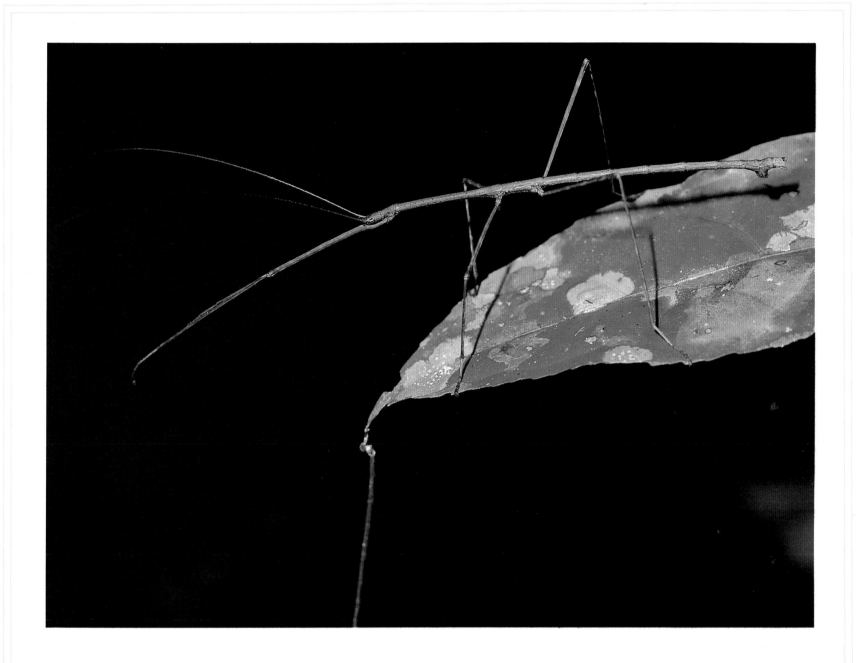

A Malaysian stick insect (Family Phasmatidae) or walking-stick would make a large and nourishing meal for a bird: hence the importance of its camouflage which, coupled with slow movements and imitative postures, makes it almost invisible among the branches.

LEFT *By day, a Garden Snail (Helix aspersa) can hide from dry air and predators inside its shell. At night, when it emerges, it is still vulnerable to some predators, but safer from dehydration.*

HEARING

When darkness removes the advantage of vision, animals must use their other senses. Sounds travel better by night, when the bustle of day is stilled. Many nocturnal animals, denied the use of their eyes, make use of specially sensitive hearing.

OPPOSITE PAGE
Vampire Bats (Desmodus rotundus) *inspire horror in humans because of their habit of drinking blood, which they lap from a small incision made with very sharp teeth. They carry rabies, with which they may infect people as well as the cattle which are their usual victims.*

The Red Fox (Vulpes vulpes) *is a successful nocturnal hunter, aided by its acute senses of smell and hearing. For centuries, farmers have tried in vain to defend their small livestock against raids by this resourceful predator.*

RIGHT *A Tube-nosed Fruit Bat* (Nyctimene cephalotes) *from Sulawesi feeds mainly on fruit, flowers, and nectar. The function of the nose-tubes is not clear, but they may help to keep pollen out of the nostrils while the bat is feeding.*

*Killer Whales (*Orcinus orca*) perceive their world almost
entirely in terms of sound. Each family, or 'pod' of whales has
its own dialect, or version of the killer whale 'language'. With
their sophisticated sonar system, killer whales can distinguish
between cod and salmon at long range.*

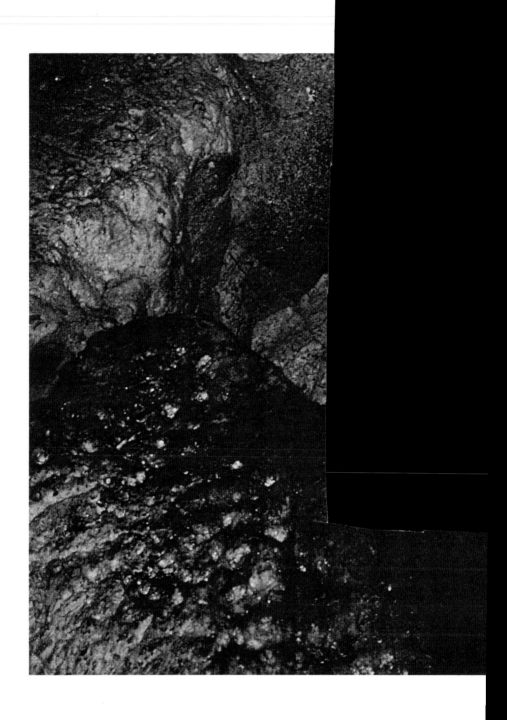

Oilbirds (Steatornis caripensis) *have strong,*
like those of birds of prey, but they use the
the wing. They navigate inside lightless caves
echoes of the clicking sounds they make th
also scream and snarl very loudly wh

False Vampire Bats (Megaderma cor) are found in the Old World tropics, from Africa to the Philippines and Australia. This is a Heart-nosed Bat, from Tanzania; it feeds mainly on insects, which it catches by sight. The large ears are to help its echo-location inside the caves where it lives.

LEFT *A Woodmouse (Apodemus sylvaticus) has sensitive eyes but rather poor vision, so that it can see movements but not a clear image. At night, it relies more on its hearing to warn it of the approach of danger.*

The Eastern Quoll (Dasyurus viverrinus), *from Australia, is a nocturnal carnivore, which hunts by a combination of three senses. It has a sensitive nose, large eyes, and well-developed hearing. Once, quolls were destroyed by poultry keepers, but now they are known to do more good than harm, by killing rats and invertebrate pests.*

RIGHT *A Black-tailed Jack Rabbit* (Lepus californicus) *in Arizona, like others of its kind, listens intently while it is feeding at night, alert for the approach of danger. In rainy or very windy weather, when sounds might be masked, rabbits feed in daylight.*

Bat-eared Foxes (Otocyon megalotis) *in Etosha National Park, Namibia. With their huge sensitive ears they can hear the movements of their insect prey. The ears also help the fox to lose heat during the day. Unlike all other carnivores, bat-eared foxes have extra small molar teeth, for grinding up insects.*

LEFT *A Common Genet* (Genetta genetta) *is a small but efficient nocturnal predator, common in Africa and southern Europe. It listens for prey, moving very quietly, because its prey is already listening for it.*

A Barn Owl's (Tyto alba) hearing is so acute that it can judge
from the sounds alone in which direction its prey is moving.
The asymmetrical position of its ears enables it to judge
direction in both vertical and horizontal planes.

RIGHT Bats use echo-location as other animals use sight. Here, a
Daubenton's Bat (Myotis daubentonii) in the Netherlands
swoops low to investigate a falling leaf in case it is an insect.
Closer inspection showed that the item was not edible, and the
bat moved away.

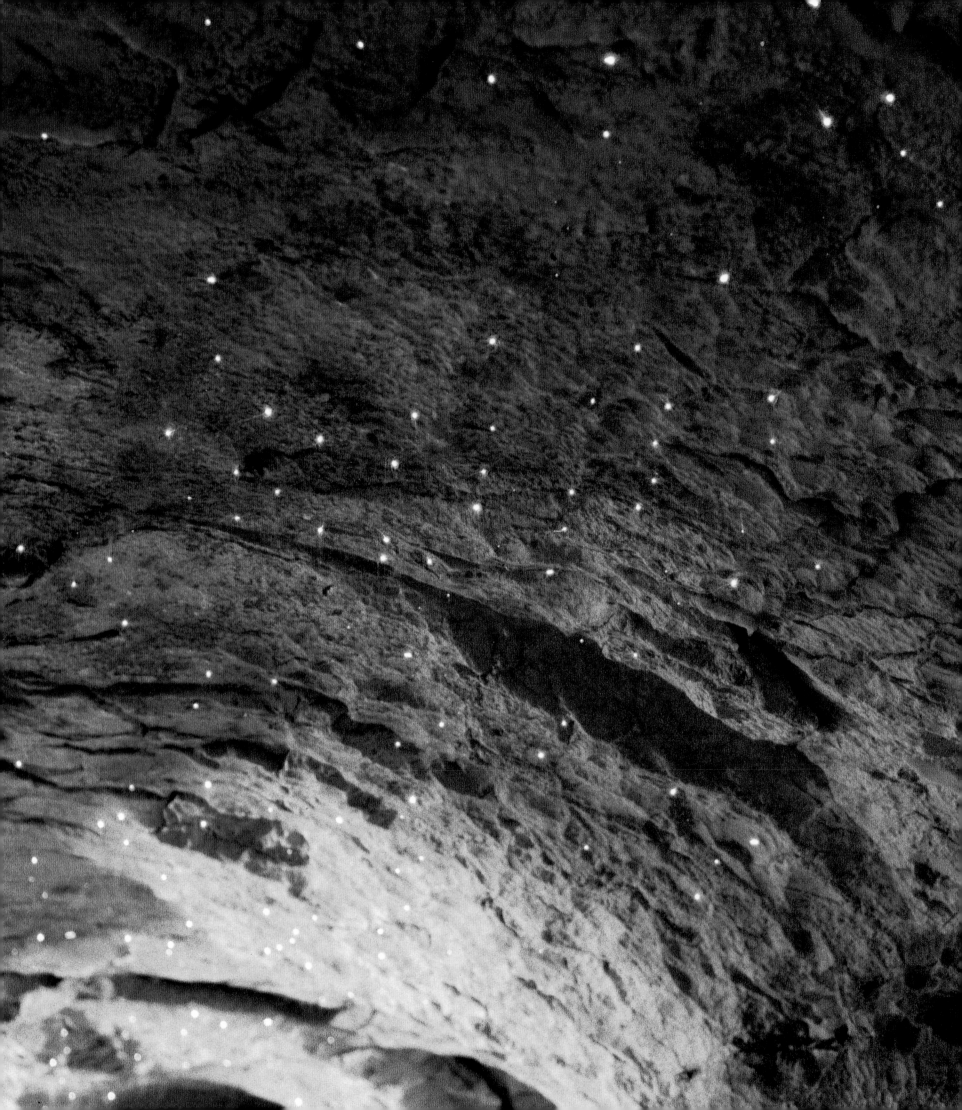

MESSAGES

Signalling one to another, animals keep in touch with other members of
their group, seek mates, or warn competitors to keep their distance. Sound
is important, but there are other media for these messages between
nocturnal animals.

A Tokay Gecko (Gekko gekko), *from Indonesia, is the largest of its kind. The male has a loud voice with which it calls to others, making a barking sound usually written down as 'toh-kay' - hence its name.*

The Long-tailed Salamander (Eurycea longicauda), *seen here in Carolina, USA, having no lungs, obtains oxygen through its moist skin, or the lining of its mouth, both of which are well supplied with blood vessels. Salamanders communicate by scent, being deaf and almost blind.*

The rich and complex nocturnal song of the Nightingale
(Luscinia megarhynchos) is one of the wonders of European
bird life. With such a voice, the Nightingale has no need of fine
feathers.

LEFT *A Yellow-crowned Night Heron (Nycticorax violaceus)*
displaying. Although these birds feed at night, they display in
daylight, when their partners can see their elegant plumage. The
raised back plumes of the male form a halo round his head as
he bows to the female.

A Gray Tree Frog (Hyla versicolor), *in full song in Michigan, USA. Frogs respond only to calls of their own kind, ignoring all others as if they could not hear them.*

LEFT ABOVE *A Spring Peeper Frog* (Hyla crucifer). *The inflated pouches beside its head act as resonators, so that its call carries as far as possible.*

LEFT BELOW *A male Edible Frog* (Rana esculenta) *joins the chorus. Its low-pitched sound travels efficiently across water, repelling other males, and attracting females that are ready to lay their eggs.*

The howling music of wolves (Canis lupus) has been closely
studied. Analysis shows that all wolves' voices are different:
they can identify each other from a distance, especially in the
still of the night. It is partly this eerie nocturnal conversation
which has made wolves so feared, and persecuted.

LEFT Red Howler Monkeys (Alouatta seniculus) in Venezuela
call to defend their group territory. Their massed cry has been
likened to the sound made by the crowd at a football match.
Groups of as many as thirty monkeys make a sound that can be
heard for several miles in the forest.

*A female Crested Newt (Triturus cristatus) lacks the crest which
gives the species its name. During courtship, she responds partly
to the colours of the male and his energetic display, but partly
also to water-borne hormones which he wafts towards
her with his tail.*

A Portuguese Fire Salamander (Salamandra salamandra) *is a colourful terrestrial species, though its young develop in water. Its sense of smell works as well on land as in water, and is an important means of communication. Its striking coloration warns would-be predators that it is distasteful.*

A Western Spadefoot Toad (Scaphiopus hammondi), *from the dry south-west of the United States, must mate as soon as possible after the first rains fall, to give its young a full three weeks to develop before the desert dries up again.*

LEFT *The Eastern Mud Salamander* (Pseudotriton montarus), *from the south-eastern United States, escapes from its enemies by burrowing into the muddy ground. Undisturbed it flourishes among damp leaves. Like other salamanders, it is almost completely blind and deaf, and communicates mainly by scent.*

Fireflies (Family Lampyridae) *in south-east Asia synchronise
their flashes, in a dramatic display at breeding time.*

RIGHT *A female European Glowworm* (Lampyris noctiluca) *is
completely flightless. She produces her light from organs under
the tip of her abdomen, raising her tail so that the light can be
seen by males flying above.*

SEEING IN THE DARK

No animal can see in total darkness, but wherever there is a glimmer of
light, specially adapted eyes can make use of it, to hide from
predators, or to hunt.

OPPOSITE PAGE

A Galago, or Lesser Bush Baby *(*Galago senegalensis*) from
Africa has the typical large eyes of nocturnal species. It leaps
among the trees in pursuit of insects, making the best use of
whatever light is available. When there is no light it is
immobilised, unable to risk a leap in the dark.*

The night life of chameleons (Chamaeleo chamaeleon) is not very active, but it is made dangerous by the abundance of predators. Chameleons feed only during the day, when they can see to 'shoot' their prey with their long, extendable tongue. Each spends the night in a fixed roost, often on a thin twig where the approach of a predator will wake it in time to escape. Some species climb to escape, while others fold their legs and drop to the forest floor. They use their ability to change colour by turning pale at night, probably mimicking a dead leaf.

A Tasmanian Devil (Sacrophilus harrisii) *looks more
ferocious than it is. A nocturnal predator, it is too stocky and
slow to catch agile prey, and it often resorts to scavenging. Its
powerful jaws enable it to crush bones, eating even the skull of
a dead sheep. However, people who have reared them in
captivity say that they make affectionate pets, in spite of their
fierce appearance.*

LEFT *A Blotched Genet* (Genetta tigrina) *in South Africa shows
the green eye-colour caused by light shining off the tapetum, the
reflective layer at the back of a nocturnal animal's eye.*

A family of Night Monkeys (Aotus trivirgatus) *in Tambopata Reserve in Peru sleep away the day before setting out in search of fruit at night. They are the only nocturnal monkeys, taking their share of the food supply while others are asleep.*

*An Angwantibo (Arctocebus calabarensis), or Golden Potto,
climbs at night amongst forest trees in West Africa. Its hands
are modified for grasping branches, with the first and second
fingers much reduced. It feeds on insects, especially caterpillars,
snails, and fruit.*

The African Wood Owl (Ciccaba woodfordi)*, like most other owls, has to be able to turn its head through more than 180° because it cannot move its eyes within their sockets.*

LEFT *The difference between the nocturnal eyes of predator and prey are summed up here. A mouse has a wide field of view but poor focusing ability, while a Barn Owl* (Tyto alba) *has a narrow field and can focus well at short range.*

*The Aye-aye (Daubentonia madagascariensis), a solitary and
secretive lemur from Madagascar, finds its food by tapping on
the trunk of a tree and listening for the movements of grubs
under the bark. It uses its sharp teeth and long middle finger to
gnaw away the bark and extract the grub.*

LEFT *A Grey Heron (Ardea cinerea), a diurnal fisherman, shows
the third eyelid, or nictitating membrane, used by many
nocturnal birds to protect their eyes against bright light. A fish
scale in the corner of its mouth is evidence of its last meal.*

*In weak light, a gecko's pupils are fully expanded to admit as
much light as possible. A gecko (Hemidactylus turcicus) has no
moveable eyelids: they have evolved to become transparent, and
are permanently closed to protect the eyeball.*

The pupil of a Giant Forest Gecko (Gekko stentor) contracts in daylight to a narrow slit. Four small openings enable the gecko to maintain a partial view of its surroundings.

The Spectral Tarsier (Tarsius spectrum) has the largest eyes for its size of any animal. It lives in Sulawesi, feeding on insects and lizards at night in the forest. Its local name means 'ghostly animal', reflecting its silent, flitting progress among the trees. Its large ears and eyes make it look like a bush baby, but it is classified in the group of primates that includes monkeys, apes and humans.

A Mouse Lemur (Microcebus murinus), *from the dry forests of western Madagascar, moves among the trees on fine branches among dense foliage. It is completely nocturnal, as are many of the smallest lemurs, feeding on insects and small vertebrates.*

RIGHT *A Slow Loris* (Nycticebus coucang) *in Malaysia sleeps all day curled up in a tree. By night, it hunts for insects and birds' eggs in the trees, only rarely coming to the ground. It has very strong hands and feet, with the thumbs and big toes opposable to enable it to grip branches.*

SMELL

When vision is denied, some animals have developed their sense of smell to find food or a mate. A strolling dog knows its territory by sight, but at night it reads the scents of the hedgerow like an evening newspaper. Other more specialized animals have carried this sensitivity to extremes.

OPPOSITE PAGE
The Deer Mouse (Peromyscus maniculatus) lives all over North America, from Canada to Mexico. It is one of the species that keeps the great western forests in good condition by sniffing out truffles and spreading their spores in its droppings.

In South and Central America, the Tamandua (Tamandua
tetradactyla) is a forest anteater, living in trees and foraging at
night for termites' nests among the branches, using its highly-
developed sense of smell. During the day it sleeps in a hollow
tree, safe from predators.

LEFT The Ringtail Possum (Pseudocheirus peregrinus) lives in
the forests of Australia. Its tail is prehensile, enabling it to move
safely among the branches at night. Its diet includes the
aromatic leaves of eucalyptus trees, which are toxic to many
other animals.

A Grass Snake (Natrix natrix) *uses its tongue to sample the air, returning the sample to paired Jacobson's organs inside its jaw.*

RIGHT ABOVE *The Gila Monster* (Heloderma suspectum) *of the south-western USA is mainly nocturnal, ponderously tasting its way across the desert floor.*

RIGHT BELOW *the Tuatara* (Sphenodon punctactus) *is forced to be nocturnal by two factors: its prey, a giant cricket, is strictly nocturnal; and its burrows are taken over at night for part of the year by nesting shearwaters.*

A Hairy-nosed Wombat (Lasiorhinus latifrons) *in Australia spends the day sleeping in a burrow underground. At night, it emerges to eat grass, digesting it slowly during the day in a specially elongated intestine.*

LEFT *The Two-toed Sloth* (Choloepus didactylus) *lives only in the rainforests of Central and South America. It feeds on leaves, twigs, and fruit, moving about – slowly – at night, and hanging still by day to avoid predators such as Harpy Eagles and Jaguars.*

Polecats (Mustela putorius) *use their sense of smell to hunt but their own smell to communicate with each other. Musk glands located under the tail produce a pungent-smelling fluid which is used to mark territories.*

LEFT ABOVE The Kiwi of New Zealand (Apteryx australis) *finds food by smell, using nostrils at the tip of a flexible bill.*

LEFT BELOW The Large Tree Shrew (Tupaia tana), *in spite of its name, lives mainly on the ground, sniffing round the dark forest floor for insects such as cockroaches and beetles.*

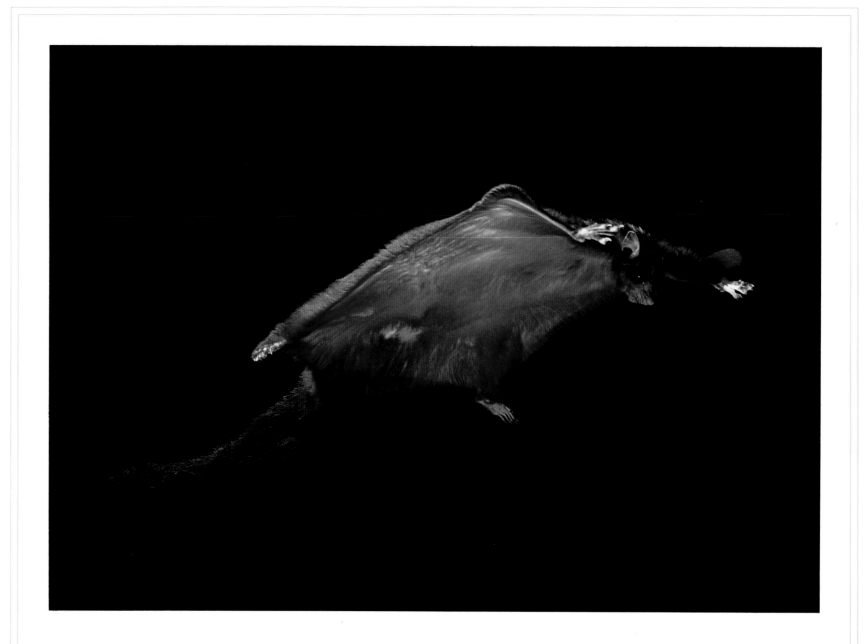

A Spotted Giant Flying Squirrel (Petaurista elegans), *from Java,
glides as far as 450 metres (490 yards) from tree to tree. It feeds
on nuts, fruit, shoots and young leaves. By day, it hides in a
hollow tree. (Local people hunt the squirrels for meat).*

RIGHT *Hedgehogs* (Erinaceus europaeus) *are nocturnal predators
on slugs, snails, and earthworms. They hunt by scent, sniffing
boldly through hedgerows and gardens; some have been known
to cover more than 3 km (2 miles) in a single night's foraging.
During their journeys, they are very vulnerable to being
hit by cars.*

A Fat-tailed Dunnart (Sminthopsis crassicaudata), *sometimes*
called a Marsupial Mouse, is Australia's equivalent to a shrew.
A small but fierce nocturnal predator, it is capable of killing and
eating insects as long as itself (8 cm or 3 ins). It can store fat in
its tail during good times, for use when food is harder to find.

LEFT *The European Weasel (Mustela Nivalis) is the smallest*
carnivore. It is related to the Polecat, but it is modified to chase
prey underground. This one has caught a Yellow-necked Mouse
(Apodemus flavicollis), which it is carrying back to its lair.

The female Vapourer (Orgyia antiqua) is flightless. She remains on the empty cocoon, pumping out her pheromone until a male arrives to mate with her. She will lay her eggs on the tree where she hatched: the caterpillars migrate to new sites before they pupate in their turn.

LEFT *A male Vapourer Moth (Orgyia antiqua) searches the air for traces of the pheromone, or aerial hormone, produced by females. Its feathery antennae can pick up the scent from several miles away, even in smelly city centres. It follows the gradient from weaker to stronger until it finds a mate.*

SIXTH SENSES AND OTHERS

Vision, smell, and hearing are all senses within our own capacities.
Nocturnal animals have developed other senses which we lack. The ability
to see heat, or to sense electrical fields, are among the secret weapons of
an army of nocturnal animals.

The Electric Knife Fish (Sternarchus albifrons) *lives in the
murky waters of the Amazon, feeding on the larvae of midges
and worms in the mud at the bottom. It detects its prey by
producing a weak electric field, and detecting changes in the
response from its surroundings.*

This species of Fer-de-lance (Bothrops asper) is found in the rainforests of Central and South America, where it hunts small mammals, finding them at night by sensing the heat of their bodies by means of pit organs below its eyes. Its venom causes severe internal bleeding, swiftly killing its prey.

Dung beetles (Family Scarabidae) like this species from the rainforest of Costa Rica, find the dung they need to feed their offspring by its scent, often from great distances as they fly among the trees.

The Electric Eel (Electrophorus electricus) *has a powerful electric organ, capable of producing 550 volts and nearly 2 amperes of current. This shock, lasting only two thousandths of a second, is sufficient to stun prey. It also produces a slow, weak pulse of about 1 volt, which it uses to explore its surroundings.*

RIGHT *An Elephant Trunk Fish* (Gnathonemus petersi) *in West Africa finds its way about by feeling and smelling its surroundings with the barbs on its chin. It is also weakly electric, producing a small field from organs on its underside.*

A Blind Cavefish (Anoptichthys jordani) *has only rudimentary eyes, since it has no need of vision in its lightless environment. Instead, its body is covered in tiny sensory bumps, with which it detects the smallest movement in the water.*

LEFT *The Electric Ray or Torpedo* (Torpedo marmaorata), *found in the eastern Atlantic from France to South Africa, can produce a 10 ampere current at 200 volts to kill its prey. It also uses this powerful shock in defence if handled or trodden on.*

A Black-tailed Prairie Dog (Cynomys ludovicianus) *takes the*
sun in Montana, USA. Prairie dogs are typical nocturnal prey
animals, alert to danger, with a series of alarm signals which
may be raised by any member of the family group.

LEFT ABOVE *A European Red Fox* (Vulpes vulpes) *seen on*
infra-red film.

LEFT BELOW *We cannot know exactly what a pit viper senses*
with its pit organs, but with a heat-sensitive camera we can get
some idea. In this image, yellow and red represent the warmest
part of the mouse.

FEAR OF THE DARK

Throughout the history of the human race darkness has been synonymous with danger. Humans are fearful creatures even in daylight. Uniquely among animals, we are aware of potential problems, which exist only in the abstract. Darkness compounds these fears, as the imagination works overtime to compensate for our lack of information. We are in awe of nocturnal animals because of their senses, which give them the ability to respond to surroundings invisible to us. This is why so many of them are feared and persecuted.

OPPOSITE PAGE
The blue glow from the tapetum of a domestic cat (Felis domesticus) indicates that it is a truly nocturnal animal. Light passes the sensitive cells of the retina twice, producing a rather blurred image, but making the best use of what little light is available.

FEAR OF THE DARK

'Men fear death as children fear to go in the dark; and as that natural fear in children is increased with tales, so is the other.'

Francis Bacon, 1561-1626

It is not just children who 'fear to go in the dark'. The tales that increase our fear of darkness and death alike are part of the heritage of all races in all ages, confronting the unknown with a series of 'what if?' questions. What if the dead could come alive again? What if a man could be made out of parts of corpses? Bram Stoker and Mary Shelley, nineteenth-century authors of *Dracula* and *Frankenstein*, were not breaking new ground when they wrote their classic novels; they were building on an ancient combination of fear and fascination with the idea of death that has held the human race in thrall since humans first learned to think and share their feelings.

Darkness has a similar effect. The writer O. Henry's last words, 'Turn up the lights, I don't want to go home in the dark', were a quotation from a popular song of the time that expressed the common fear of the night. (Used by him, they expressed also a rare bravado in the face of everlasting darkness, which is why they are remembered.) Ghost stories and fairy tales have darkness and the night as a regular theme. The fear of darkness is graphically expressed by the poet John Milton, for example, when he describes Samson's blindness.

Poets and other writers who have celebrated the beauty of the night have usually done so in terms of the company they were in at the time, or the light of the moon and stars. They never hymn the absence of light, and least of all the sounds, little or large, coming from beyond the blindfold of darkness.

How is it that this ancient fear has survived into the age of electric light indoors and out, and the extinction or exile into parks and reserves of most of humanity's natural enemies?

To find the answer, we must delve deep into the past, long before the age of writing, to a time when our earliest primate ancestors were beginning to establish themselves as dominant animals on the savannah grasslands of Africa. At that time, two fears became ingrained into the primate psyche: the fear of darkness and the fear of snakes. To this day, a naive chimpanzee shown its first snake will react with fear and loathing, even though it will handle similarly shaped objects, such as pieces of rope, with no reluctance at all. In much the same way, it will move from a dark place to a lit area whenever it has the choice, which it seldom has in the wild. Experiments have shown that much the same is true of humans, and from a very early age.

Even today, humans are vulnerable to powerful predators in certain parts of the world. It is easy to understand why the rural African is reluctant to walk in the bush at night, or the Indian in the jungle. Lions and tigers, to them, are not the stuff of children's tales, but very real neighbours. It is equally simple to empathize with the city-dweller in Los Angeles, for example, where predators of a different kind roam the darkened streets. But why does a rustle in the bushes beside a quiet country lane at night set the neck bristling, the heart racing, and the adrenalin flowing, in an industrialized country where the largest predator is the shy fox? The cause lies not with the darkness itself, nor yet with the tales told to us as children, but with the deeply ingrained fears of our ancient ancestors, on which the lasting success of those tales is based.

These fears arise from our sense of disadvantage in the dark. The poor, purblind, stumbling human is surrounded at night by other animals gliding and swooping, stalking and fleeing, all of which know where they are going and what they are doing at a time when a human is at a loss. Owls have been thought to have magical powers for many centuries, just because they can apparently see, and catch agile prey, in total darkness. Moths inspire horror in many otherwise rational people, who may murmur something about the danger of getting scales in one's eyes. Bats are feared, it is said, because people are afraid that they will become entangled in their hair. The real reason, rearing itself from the dark (that word again!) depths of the subconscious, is that these creatures have senses that we can barely begin to understand.

Combine this awe of creatures possessing uncanny senses with the universal fear of snakes, and then consider the position of pit vipers in the popularity polls! Like bats, many of their species are endangered, and again like bats, their only real hope of survival is in gaining the sympathy and support of humans. Sadly, like most species of bats, they are disliked, or at best mistrusted, by most of the human race. The annual rattlesnake round-ups in the southern United States testify to the murderous feelings of people towards these reptiles. When feelings stem from such deep-seated fears as these, there is little hope of changing them in time to offer much chance of a long-term future to the bats or to the snakes. The fact that bats pollinate many valuable crops and ornamental plants, or that pit vipers control the numbers of animals regarded as vermin by farmers, weigh very light in the balance with ancient fear on the other side.

Yet we find nocturnal animals fascinating as well as fearsome. It does not seem out of the question that we might respect them and give them room to live, rather than annihilating them because they give affront to our sense of what animals ought to be able to do. In the broader view, is it not more reassuring to be abroad in a night alive with the song of crickets, the bustle of shrews and the hoot of owls, the brush of a moth's wing and the flutter of a bat, rather than in a night silent and dead, save for the noise of traffic and the distant howling of police sirens?

INDEX

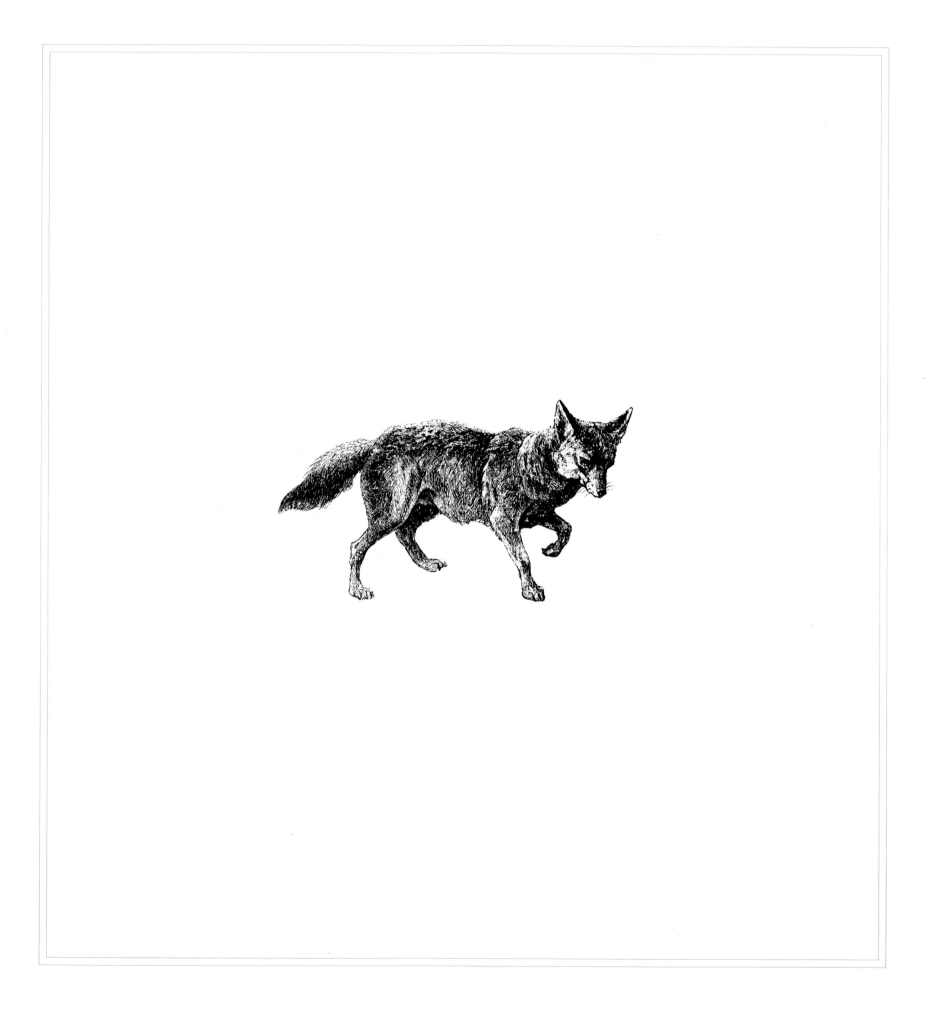